This SpongeBob SquarePants Annual belongs to

Daniel

Age 9

My Favourite character is

Patrick

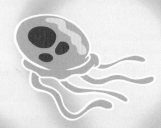

Contents

EGMONT

We bring stories to life

First published in Great Britain in 2010
by Egmont UK Limited,
239 Kensington High Street, London W8 6SA

Written by Brenda Apsley. Designed by Catherine Ellis.

ISBN 978 1 4052 5250 8
1 3 5 7 9 10 8 6 4 2
Printed in Italy

Welcome!
I'm HOOKED on happiness, Patrick! How about you?
I SHORE am too, SpongeBob!

Way Back When ...

Long ago, the undersea town of Bikini Bottom was home to barking worms, stinging jellyfish, flying clams – and a stone-age sea sponge called SpongeGar and his friends Patar the starfish and Squog the octopus.

Squillions of years later, that same sea-town is home to smiley sea sponge **SpongeBob SquarePants**. Squishy, squashy, squidgy, squeezy and squelchy (and sometimes just plain spongey), he's one happy sponge.

Happiness is catching and I've got the bug!

King of the spatula, this fry cook has one wish: to be named Krusty Krab Employee of the Month.

Ride 'em! How many salty seahorses? Circle the number.

1 2 3 4 5 6 ⑦ 8 9 10

Ahm tha ka-rah-tay queen!
Meow!

Rip-roarin' rodent **Sandy Cheeks** loves lionfish fighting, sand sledding, clam wrestling and anchor tossing. If it's dangerous, she'll do it.

Squidward Tentacles dislikes most things, apart from his clarinet. Problem is, when he plays it, the Bikini Bottomites have to protect their ears, and sales of Super Strong Spongey Earplugs soar.

SpongeBob's best friend **Patrick Star** sleeps, snoozes, naps and ZZZZZZZs under his Rock home. He'd like to answer life's big question, if only he could remember what it is ...

SpongeBob's pet is **Gary**, a one-word snail.

A seaful of soaky starfish!

Count, and write the total in the box.

8

Answer: there are 8 starfish and 7 seahorses.

Rivals!

Born on the same day, Eugene H Krabs and Sheldon Q Plankton became bitter rivals when Mr Krabs grew up to be a **money-making crustacean of genius** and Plankton ... didn't.

Serve it up and make me money!

Mr Krabs made his lobster-pot Krusty Krab into the finest eating establishment ever established for making money. Thanks to SpongeBob flipping thousands of Triple Supreme Krabby Patties, it's success on a sea-plate.

Making Cents:

Mr Krabs loves every **CENT** he makes. Can you find 9 cents, spelled out left to right and top to bottom?

A	C	E	N	T	C
C	E	N	T	C	E
E	N	L	P	E	N
N	T	C	E	N	T
T	C	E	N	T	R
M	Q	C	E	N	T

Next to money, Mr Krabs loves Pearl, his whale of a daughter, and Cashey the cash register, the closest thing to a friend he's ever had.

Plankton's rival eatery, the Chum Bucket, is always open ... and always empty. From the time his computer wife Karen opens up, it remains unloved, unclean and unvisited, even by Plankton's millions of micro-relatives.

CHUM BUCKET

CHUM BURGER
CHUM FRIES
CHUM SHAKE
CHUM ON A STICK
CHUMBALAYA **NEW**
CHUM CHILI
CHUM PIE

WARNING:

Plankton may be microscopic, but he has a big plan: to steal the super-secret Krabby Patty recipe and make his fortune.

He tried hiding out in SpongeBob's brain, then tried to trick him into singing the recipe. Both plots failed, but he will try again – if he doesn't get stepped on first ...

Tick ✓ Plankton's full name:

a. Smelldon U Plankton

b. Shelly O'Plankerton

c. Sheldon Q Plankton ✓

SPONGEBOB SQUAREPANTS

ROTTEN RECIPE

WELL, SHELDON, HOW DID TODAY'S EVIL SCHEME GO?

DON'T ASK, KAREN.

I'LL NEVER STEAL THAT RECIPE! NEVER!

WELL, MY ANALYSIS SHOWS THERE'S SOMETHING EVEN MORE IMPORTANT THAN THE KRABBY PATTY RECIPE...

...THE FRY COOK!

YOU MEAN I SHOULD STEAL SPONGEBOB?

NO, YOU SHOULD GET HIM TO STOP MAKING KRABBY PATTIES!

BRILLIANT! BUT... HOW?

Story: David Lewman. Pencils: Gregg Schigiel. Inks: Jeff Albrecht. Colour: Wes Dzioba. Lettering: Comicraft. SpongeBob SquarePants created by Stephen Hillenburg.

12

AND SO...

AHRR, SPONGEBOB! I, *MR. KRABS*, HAVE TAKEN MY...ER...ME KRABBY PATTIES OFF THE MENU! I COMMAND YOU TO STOP MAKING THEM!

AHOY, UM, MATEY!

HA, HA! VERY FUNNY, MR. KRABS! YOU SURE CAN MAKE ME LAUGH! YOU'RE THE BEST BOSS EVER!

HELLO...ER... *HOWDY*, SPONGEBOB! I AM A-BEGGING YOU, PARDNER! STOP RUSTLIN' UP THEM KRABBY PATTIES!

VERY FUNNY, SANDY! YOU'RE THE BEST FRIEND EVER!

HEY!

SPOOOOOONGEBOB!

STOP MAKING ME... FOREVER!

VERY FUNNY, DREAM KRABBY PATTY! YOU'RE THE BEST NIGHTMARE EVER!

THAT FOOL WILL *NEVER* STOP MAKING KRABBY PATTIES!

AND I'M RUNNING OUT OF COSTUMES!

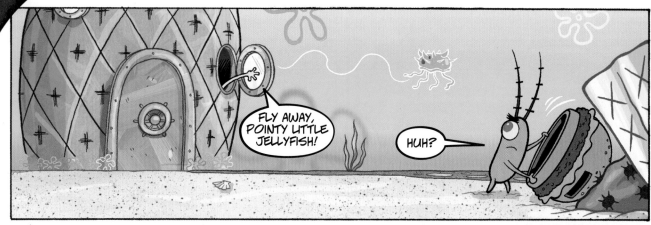

AND SO ENDS ANOTHER WONDERFUL DAY AT THE WONDERFUL KRUSTY KRAB!

PSSSSST! SPONGEBOB!

WHAT'S THIS? A TALKING ROCK?

NO, YOU IDIOT--I MEAN, PAL. IT'S ME, PLANKTON.

MR. KRABS TOLD ME NOT TO TALK TO YOU!

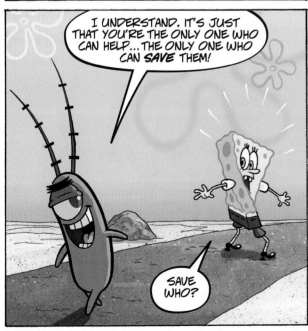

I UNDERSTAND. IT'S JUST THAT YOU'RE THE ONLY ONE WHO CAN HELP...THE ONLY ONE WHO CAN **SAVE** THEM!

SAVE WHO?

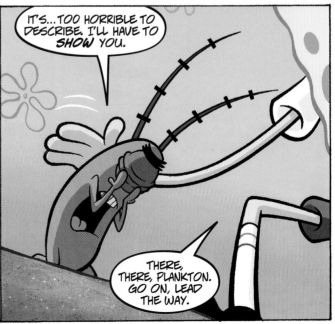

IT'S...TOO HORRIBLE TO DESCRIBE. I'LL HAVE TO **SHOW** YOU.

THERE, THERE, PLANKTON. GO ON, LEAD THE WAY.

13

ARE THOSE **HOT PEPPERS**?

THEY ARE **NOW**...

WHAT'S THIS ALL ABOUT? WHY ARE THEY DOING THIS TO THOSE POOR VEGETABLES?

WELL, MY **INNOCENT** FRIEND, THIS PLACE IS WHERE THEY MAKE...

...**KRABBY PATTIES**!

AAAAGGHHH!

CA-CHUNK

THOSE POOR VEGETABLES! I'VE GOT TO RESCUE THEM!

YOU CAN'T! THOSE MACHINES WILL DICE YOU ALIVE!

THIS IS THE WORST DAY EVER...

YOU KNOW, THERE IS **ONE** THING YOU COULD DO...

LATER, AT THE KRUSTY KRAB...

SQUIDWARD! WHERE'S SPONGEBOB?

HE SAID SOMETHING ABOUT QUITTING FOREVER. I'M **SO** HAPPY...

WHAT?!!!

SPONGEBOB! GET OUT HERE! **NOW!**

BANG! BANG! BANG!

AND...

...SO IT'S NO USE, MR. KRABS. I'LL NEVER COOK ANOTHER KRABBY PATTY. I'VE SEEN HOW THEY'RE MADE.

OH, YE HAVE...?

LATER...

I'M WARNING YOU, MR. KRABS! ONCE YOU PULL THAT DOOR OPEN, YOU'LL SEE THE HORRIBLE, SCARY...

...BACK OF THE CHUM BUCKET?

THOOOOM

COME ON. I'LL SHOW YEH HOW THE PATTIES ARE *REALLY* MADE-- AT THE KRUSTY KRAB.

SQUISH

CURSES!

IT'S SO... *BEAUTIFUL!*

LOCK

NOW WILL YEH GET BACK TO FRYIN' UP KRABBY PATTIES?

YES, SIR!

GOOD THING HE DIDN'T ASK WHERE *KETCHUP* COMES FROM...

THE END

Puzzled with Patrick

Want to work your brain cells harder than you've ever worked them before? Well, prepare for Patrick's puzzles!

Safe

Where does Mr Krabs keep the secret Krabby Patty recipe book?

It's in SpongeBob's head.

Souvenir

Colour in the shapes with a spot and see what's left. Think you know what the mystery object is?

It's the grain of sand I brought back from Mussel Beach.

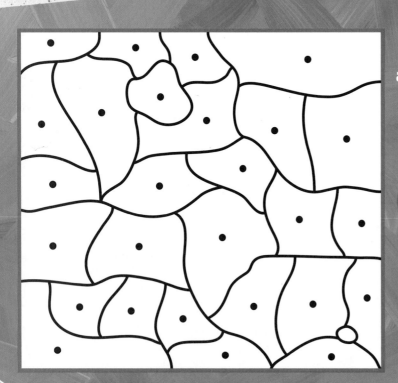

Story and art: Bob Flynn. Colour: Wes Dzioba. Lettering: Comicraft. *SpongeBob SquarePants* created by Stephen Hillenburg.

HOLD THAT POSE!

SMILE, PLEASE!

SpongeBob is really snap-happy since he got his new camera. But it has its own mind when it comes to what pictures to take – often clicking away before SpongeBob has had chance to say 'cheese'! The results are, well, see for yourself …

Help SpongeBob match these photos of his friends to their name labels.

Plankton, H

Patrick, D

a

b

Squidward, C

It sure was hard to get Gary to come out of his shell!

e

d

Mrs Puff, F

Don't give up the day job!

SpongeBob's pictures aren't exactly perfect. Do you
know what job he does each day? Tick the box.

☐ lifeguard   ☐ parrot trainer   ☑ fry cook

Mr Krabs. C

Gary. B

Sandy. A

Pearl. E

f

e

g

h

SpongeBob SquarePants

BELLY UNBUTTONED

HI, PAT! WHATCHA DOIN'?

OH, HEY, SPONGEBOB!

I'M MAKING A LINT KITTY!

OH, MY! HOW DID YOU DO IT?

EASY! I JUST USED MY BELLY BUTTON LINT!

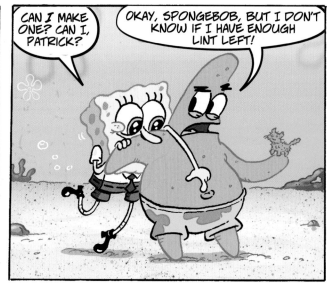

CAN I MAKE ONE? CAN I, PATRICK?

OKAY, SPONGEBOB, BUT I DON'T KNOW IF I HAVE ENOUGH LINT LEFT!

NO, SILLY! I WANT TO MAKE A KITTY OUT OF MY VERY OWN BELLY BUTTON LINT!

NOW, LET'S SEE...

...I'LL JUST...

ER... PATRICK?

Story: Cory Barba. Art: Bob Flynn. Colour: Wes Dzioba. Lettering: Comicraft. *SpongeBob SquarePants* created by Stephen Hillenburg.

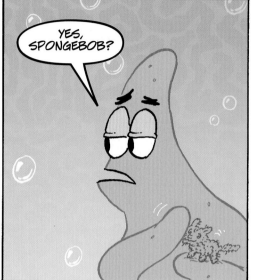

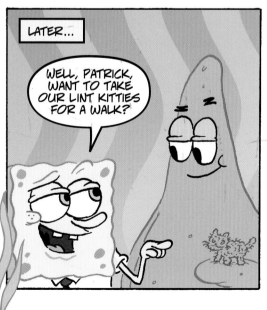

It takes a sea sponge of superior squeeziness, squelchiness and squishiness to squidge himself into the letters of the alphabet. SpongeBob is that sponge.

Happiness

Copy the coloured letter into the porthole by each SpongeFact, then rearrange them into a spongey saying.

Aaargh! What have I done?

S — When Squidward looked after SpongeBob's pet snail, it became ill. When SpongeBob came home he took the snail medicine meant for Gary and turned into ... **S**pongeSnail.

O — SpongeBob ate some **O**nion ice cream, and people started to avoid him because of his stinky breath. When Patrick said it was maybe because he was ugly, SpongeBob took to wearing a disguise ...

T — When SpongeBob StarPants hit the big time in a **T**V ad for the Krusty Krab he believed he'd quit his job. But when his fans only wanted to see him flipping patties, it was back to work.

W — When Pearl the **W**hale needed a date for the Poseidon Elementary school prom, SpongeBob tried to make himself tall, dark and handsome. Not easy for someone short, square and yellow ...

G — SpongeBob trained **G**ary to race against Snelle, Squidward's super-snail. But both trailed home in a race won by Patrick's entry ... a racing rock.

30

When SpongeBob had to write an **E**ssay he stayed up all night. He began seeing things – then that's what ended up in his essay.

The title SpongeBob craves is **E**mployee of the Month. He puts in long hours for almost no pay to earn the honour ... and the cake.

Poo-eeee!

Patrick was the only Bikini Bottomite without a **N**ose, so he got one. He liked it – until he found that there were bad smells as well as good ones.

Once, a customer accused SpongeBob of forgetting to put **P**ickles on a Krabby Patty. He was so upset that he quit, but when takings fell, Mr Krabs begged him to come back.

Happiness is a

W E T   S P O N G E!

CALCULATOR

Story: Chris Duffy. Art: Jacob Chabot. Lettering: Comicraft. Color: Wes Dzioba. SpongeBob SquarePants created by Stephen Hillenburg.

Life's a Laugh!

All right, put the money in the bag! Put it in!

Who turned out the lights?

Don't you have to be stupid somewhere else?

Not until 4:00 ...

Ever feel like you live in a bubble, SpongeBob?

Anything can happen in Patrick's Imagination Box ...

I imagined I was a starfish!

Hey, it really works!

33

THE ISLAND OF GOLDEN BARNACLES

BARNACLES!

HEY, GARY...

HAVE YOU EVER NOTICED HOW GOOD IT FEELS TO YELL "BARNACLES" WHEN SOMETHING GOES WRONG?

MEOW.

WHAT'S THE MATTER, GARY? SOMETHING ON MY BOARD?

HISS!!!

Story: David Lewman. Pencils: Gregg Schigiel. Inks: Jacob Chabot. Colour: Wes Dzioba. Lettering: Comicraft. SpongeBob SquarePants created by Stephen Hillenburg.

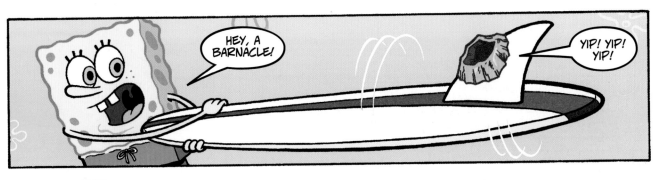

SEVERAL REST-STOPS LATER...

HOW ARE WE GOING TO FIND THE ISLAND OF GOLDEN BARNACLES?

OH, WE'LL FIND IT. HOW MANY ISLANDS CAN THERE BE?

URCHIN ISLAND...

I DON'T LIKE THIS ISLAND, SPONGEBOB. IT HURTS MY BUTT!

OYSTER ISLAND...

THIS ISLAND HURTS MY EARS!

CLACK CLACK CLACK CLACK

HAMMERHEAD SHARK ISLAND...

DON'T WORRY, PATRICK. THEY'RE JUST CALLED HAMMER-HEADS.

BARNACLES ARE SUCH **WONDROUS** CREATURES. I'VE NEVER UNDERSTOOD WHY FOREIGNERS SAY "BARNACLES!" WHEN SOMETHING GOES **AMISS!**

SHOCKING!

YES, THAT CERTAINLY IS SHOCKING.

TOTALLY SHOCKING.

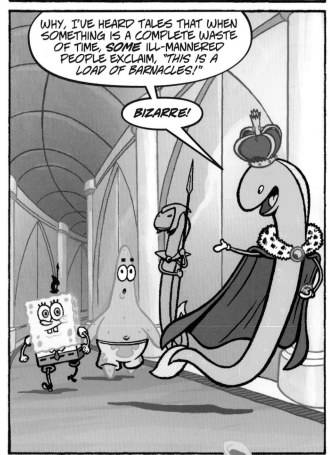

WHY, I'VE HEARD TALES THAT WHEN SOMETHING IS A COMPLETE WASTE OF TIME, **SOME** ILL-MANNERED PEOPLE EXCLAIM, "THIS IS A LOAD OF BARNACLES!"

BIZARRE!

SO BIZARRE.

REALLY BIZARRE.

THIS WHOLE BUCKET OF BARNACLES IS SO BARNACLED, IT MAKES ME WANT TO BARNACLE!

BARNACLES, BARNACLES, BARNACLES!!!

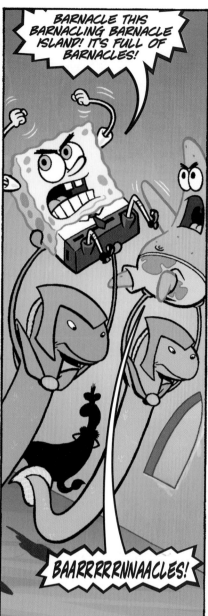

BARNACLE THIS BARNACLING BARNACLE ISLAND! IT'S FULL OF BARNACLES!

BAARRRRRNNAACLES!

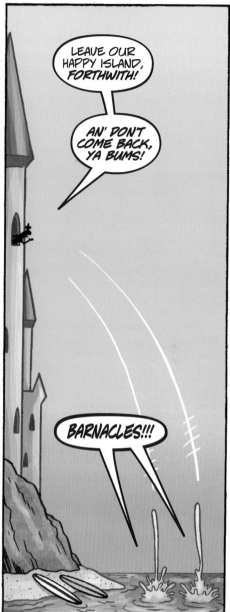

LEAVE OUR HAPPY ISLAND, FORTHWITH!

AN' DON'T COME BACK, YA BUMS!

BARNACLES!!!

ONE RETURN SURFING TRIP LATER...

IT'S SURE GOOD TO BE HOME.

OOOH, LOOK! A RARE SPOTTED CLAM! WE SHOULD TAKE *HIM* BACK HOME, TOO!

CLAMS!!!

END

Story: Jacob Lambert. Pencils: Gregg Schigiel. Inks: Jeff Albrecht. Colour: Wes Dzioba. Lettering: Comicraft. *SpongeBob SquarePants* created by Stephen Hillenburg.

SpongeBob SquareFace

happy

crazy

scared

and, when he's flipping
those pretty patties ...

love struck

Patrick, meanwhile, is ...
Patrick

48

Draw and colour in some more SpongeBob faces.

Design a new Bikini Bottomite to join the crew.
Draw, colour in and give him, her (or it) a name.

SpongeBob and Gary
started out like this ...

NAME

....

nickelodeon

SpongeBob SquarePants in THE ABOMINABLE SNOWFISH!

KNOCK KNOCK!

AH! NOTHING LIKE A WARM, COZY BED ON A QUIET SNOWY MORNING...

OH, SQUIDWARD!!

BANG BANG!

STORY BY DAVID LEWMAN PENCILS BY GREGG SCHIGIEL INKS BY ADAM DEKRAKER
COLOR BY WES DZIOBA LETTERING BY COMICRAFT

WHAT?!?

COME SLEDDING WITH US, SQUIDWARD!

WE'RE GOING TO THE SHADY SHOALS REST HOME! IT'S GOT THE SLEDDIEST SLED-HILL IN THE HISTORY OF SLEDDING!

AND THE OLDSTERS NEVER USE IT!

BEHIND THE REST HOME?! YOU MEAN YOU DON'T KNOW WHY THEY NEVER SLED DOWN THAT HILL?

UM... BECAUSE THEY'RE RESTING?

NO!

THAT HILL IS INHABITED BY THE TERRIFYING *ABOMINABLE SNOWFISH!* HE ONLY COMES OUT WHEN IT SNOWS!

OOOOH!

HOW ABOMINABLE!

SO AS MUCH AS I'D *LOVE* TO GO SLEDDING WITH YOU, I'M MUCH TOO SCARED OF THE ABOMINABLE SNOWFISH.

TH-TH-THAT'S OKAY.

W-W-WE UNDERSTAND.

HEH, HEH, HEH! "ABOMINABLE SNOWFISH!" THOSE TWO KELP-BRAINS WILL BELIEVE *ANYTHING!*

W-W-WE'RE STILL GOING SLEDDING, R-R-RIGHT?

S-S-SURE! I'M NOT SCARED OF ANY ABOMINABLE SNOWFISH! ARE Y-Y-YOU?

OF C-C-COURSE N-N-NOT!

TREMBLE

TREMBLE

TREMBLE

KNOCK

KNOCK

SINCE THOSE TWO DESTROYED ANY CHANCE I HAD OF SLEEPING IN, I MIGHT AS WELL FIX MYSELF A GOURMET BREAKFAST...

COME ON! SQUIDWARD WILL PROTECT US!

GRAWWWK!!

SQUIDWARD! SAVE US!

THAT'S FUNNY. HE'S NOT HERE.

THEN HIS STUFF WILL SAVE US!

TAKE THAT, YOU HORRIBLE MONSTER!!!

CLANG

BANG

MRRGRRUUMPH!!

BAM

GEE, THE ABOMINABLE SNOWFISH SEEMS MADDER THAN EVER!

POP

GRROARRRR!!

RUN RUN RUN RUN!!!

WHEW! THAT'S IT, PATRICK! WE'RE THROUGH RUNNING!

BECAUSE WE'RE GOING TO STAND UP TO THE SNOWFISH?

YES. PLUS I'VE GOT A CRAMP.

MURFLE... GRUMPUM... BLRRR.

I CAN'T BELIEVE IT...

THE ABOMINABLE SNOWFISH LOOKS EVEN *SCARIER* WHEN IT'S CLEANED UP!!

GAH!!

AND SOON...

STEP RIGHT UP, FOLKS! SEE THE TERRIBLE ABOMINABLE SNOWFISH!! SO UGLY, SO *HORRIBLE*, IT'LL TAKE YOUR BREATH AWAY!!

TAP

TAP

GEE, I WISH *SQUIDWARD* WERE HERE TO SEE THIS!

DONE!

Attack of the Sticky Notes

Help! Get 'em off me!

In Bikini Bottom there's a disaster waiting around every sea corner, and SpongeBob always finds it. Today it's a sticky note attack!

Decorate all the sticky notes on SpongeBob, then count and write the total in the box.

There are 12 sticky notes

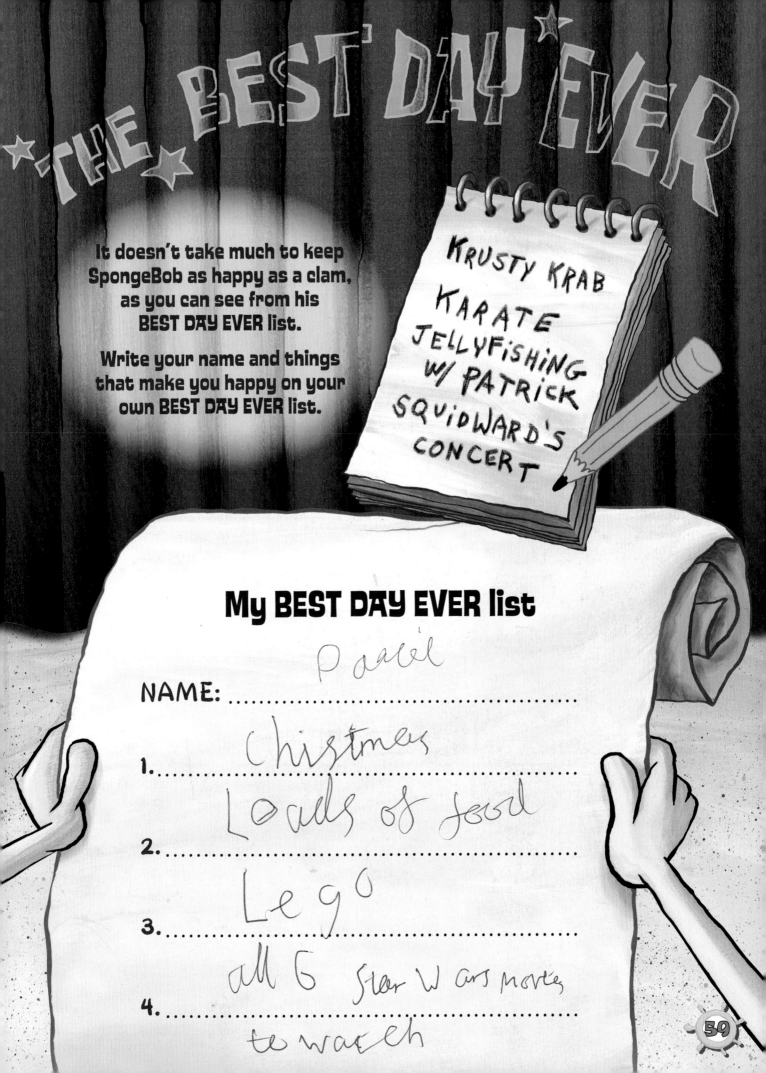

THE BEST DAY EVER

It doesn't take much to keep SpongeBob as happy as a clam, as you can see from his BEST DAY EVER list.

Write your name and things that make you happy on your own BEST DAY EVER list.

KRUSTY KRAB
KARATE
JELLYFISHING
w/ PATRICK
SQUIDWARD'S
CONCERT

My BEST DAY EVER list

NAME: Pavel

1. Christmas

2. Loads of food

3. Lego

4. all 6 Star Wars movies to watch

59

SPONGEBOB SQUAREPANTS
YAWNS

HOO, BOY! AM I EVER SLEEPY!

YAWN!

HEY, WHAT WAS THAT THING YOU JUST DID?

IT'S CALLED *YAWNING,* PATRICK!

LOOK, NOW *THAT* GUY HAS THE YAWNS.

YAWN!

FIRST ONE PERSON YAWNS, THEN IT SPREADS AROUND. IT'S LIKE THEY'RE CONTAGIOUS!

CONTAGIOUS?!

YAWN!

YAWN!

!

CONTAGIOUS CONTAGI CONTAGIOU ONTAGIOI AGIOUS CONTAGIOUS CONTA CONTAC TAGIOU

WHERE ARE YOU GOING, PATRICK?

GOTTA HIDE! HIDE FROM THE *YAWNS!!*

HOME'S NOT SAFE!

THEY GOT SQUIDWARD!

YAWN!

Story: Jacob Lambert. Pencils: Gregg Schigiel. Inks: Adam DeKraker. Colour: Wes Dzioba. Lettering: Comicraft. *SpongeBob SquarePants* created by Stephen Hillenburg.

Let's Rock!

a

b

c

d

Answer: shadow d.

Tick ✓ ONLY the equipment that the rock 'n' roll animals of the Jellyfish Jam Band need for their jam session.

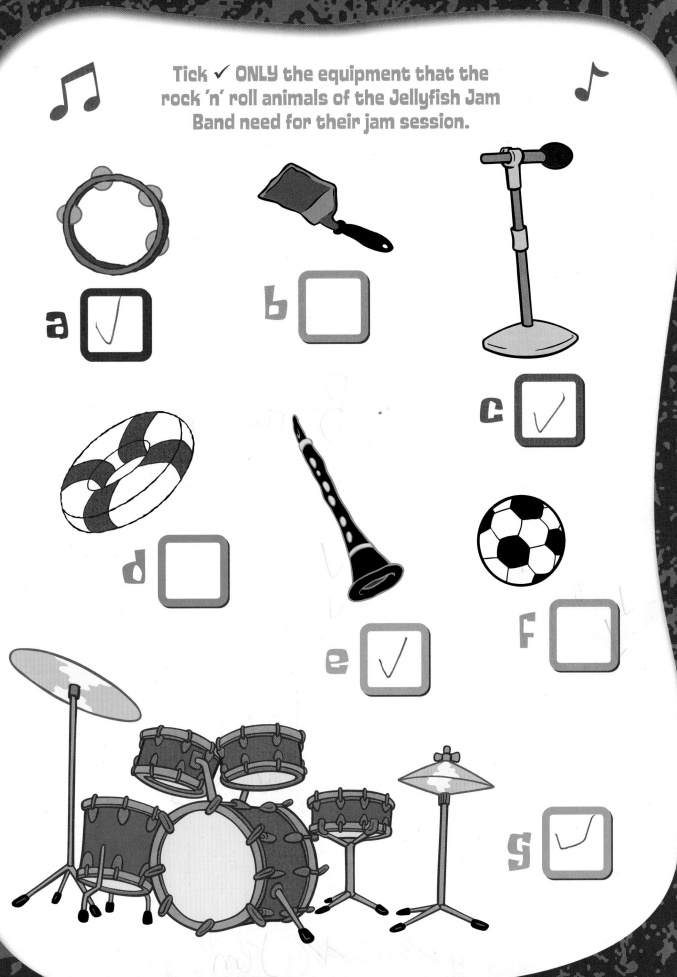

Story: Chris Duffy. Art: Jacob Chabot. Colour: Wes Dzioba. Lettering: Comicraft. *SpongeBob SquarePants* created by Stephen Hillenburg.

Best Buddies

**One picture is different from the rest.
Can you spot the odd one out?**

Answer: e is the odd one out: SpongeBob's tie is blue.

SpongeBob SmartyPants

1. Which illness turned SpongeBob into a sniffly, sneezy, nose-bubble-maker?

a. Snots   b. Suds   c. Snuffles

2. When Sandy left her pet with SpongeBob and Patrick, they panicked big-time when Wormy turned into a monster-size … what?

Butterfly

3. Tick ✓ only the towns near Bikini Bottom.

a. ☐ Barnacle Bottom   d. ☑ Rock Bottom

b. ☑ Ukelele Bottom   e. ☑ Loserburg

c. ☑ Quittersville   f. ☐ Lobster Lake

4. SpongeBob's chilli-slingin' cowboy relative was called Dead Eye.

True ☐ or False ☑

5. What was the name of the fry cook who slung his spatula before SpongeBob at the Krusty Krab?

~~Spongebob~~ Jim

6. What did Plankton make that turned everyone in the Krusty Krab into cry-babies?

a. ☐ boo hoo gas

b. ☑ goo goo gas

c. ☐ yoo too gas

7. Sandy's Treedome was invaded by what?

a. ☑ sea fleas

b. ☐ sea peas

c. ☐ sea trees

8. When an itchy-scratchy creeping sea fungus called Ick attacked everyone in Bikini Bottom, who saved them by eating it?

Gary

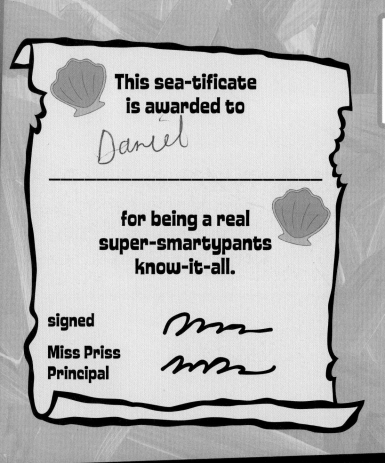

This sea-tificate is awarded to

Daniel

for being a real super-smartypants know-it-all.

signed

Miss Priss Principal

I'm waiting for the happy day when I earn my own sea-tificate from the Poseidon Academy!

Answers: 1. b, Suds. 2. butterfly. 3. b, c, d and e. 4. False, his name was SpongeBuck. 5. Jim. 6. b, goo goo gas. 7. a, sea fleas. 8. Gary.

Now Leaving ...

You are now leaving Bikini Bottom – once you've find your way through the seaweed maze!

Byeee!

Now Leaving BIKINI BOTTOM